MATTHEW CROSS
FAITH WALKER
COLLECTED

CREATED BY
CLINT D. JOHNSON

M2520.com   FaithWalkerHero.com   ChristianActionheroes.com   ClintDJohnson.com

Second Printing 2015
Published by: M25:20 Media Inc. 3183 Wilshire Blvd. #196/A53, Los Angeles, CA 90010. www.m2520.com
Email: info@m2520.com. Phone: 323-909-2520. *Matthew Cross: Faith Walker Collected* was originally published online in separate stories at www.faithwalkerhero.com between 2011 to 2014 as webcomics.

ISBN: 978-0-9907202-0-1
Library of Congress Control Number: 2014915055

CREDITS

COVER
Pencils and Inks
Steven Butler
Colors
Michael Summers
Logo Redesign
Mike Roberts

SIN ASSASSINS
Story and Pencils
Clint D. Johnson
Inks
Montos
Colors
Caesar
Lettering
Don Ensign

DELIVER US FROM EVIL
Story, Art and Lettering
Clint D. Johnson

SINS OF THE FATHER
Story
Clint D. Johnson and
Ralph Ellis Miley
Pencils
Herbert Richardson Jr.
Inks
Antonio Buffoco
Colors
Mark Melton

Interior Cover
Line Art
Gary Martin
Colors
Lisa Hutchinson

SMOKE AND MIRRORS
Story, Inks and Lettering
Clint D. Johnson
Pencils and Colors
Tim Gagnon
Additional Inks
Wayne Cash
Layouts
Jose A. Gullin and Clint D. Johnson

KEEPER OF THE CITY
Story and Art
Clint D. Johnson
Ink Assist
Steven Lyles

Edits
Bettie J. Hensley

Designer Fonts
Blambot

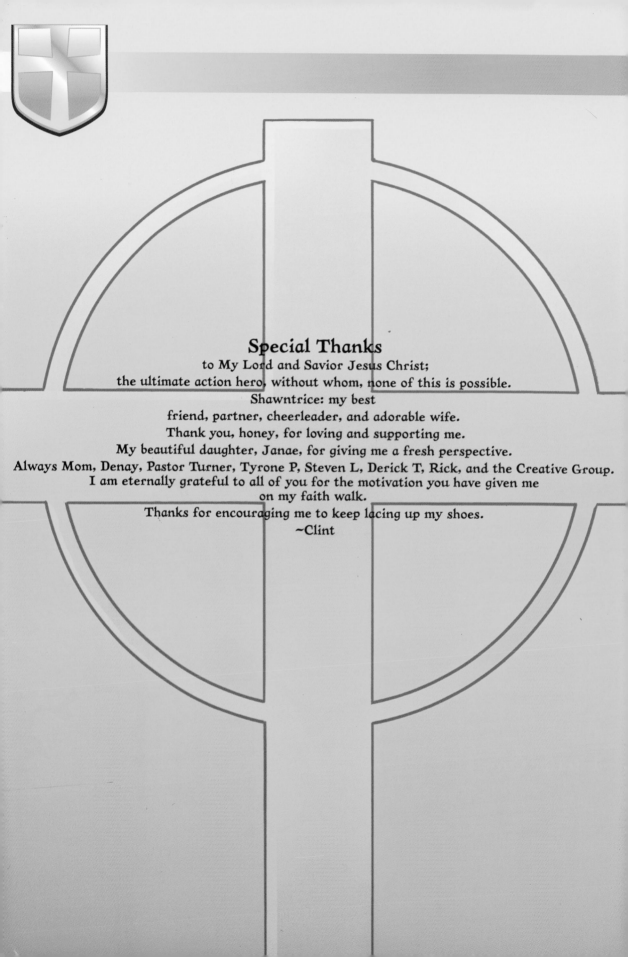

Special Thanks

to My Lord and Savior Jesus Christ;
the ultimate action hero, without whom, none of this is possible.
Shawntrice: my best
friend, partner, cheerleader, and adorable wife.
Thank you, honey, for loving and supporting me.
My beautiful daughter, Janae, for giving me a fresh perspective.
Always Mom, Denay, Pastor Turner, Tyrone P, Steven L, Derick T, Rick, and the Creative Group.
I am eternally grateful to all of you for the motivation you have given me
on my faith walk.
Thanks for encouraging me to keep lacing up my shoes.
~Clint

FOREWORD

Persevere: steady persistence in a course of action or purpose in spite of difficulties, obstacles, or discouragement. That is the very definition of our walk of faith in Christ Jesus. I met Clint D. Johnson at the San Diego Comic Con in 1996 at a gathering of Christian comic book fans in a small hotel room. From there, the Christian Comic Arts Society would have monthly meetings in the Southern California area.

That is where I was introduced to Clint's premiere character, Matthew Cross, Faith Walker. He created the character in 1990. *Faith Walker* appeared as a comic strip in the *Los Angeles Community Clipper*, which ran from 1990-1994; this fact would probably make *Faith Walker* the longest running African American Christian superhero series.

Faith Walker's first appearance in a comic book occurred in 1998, and in that same year there was play that was produced with him as the central character. During these 24 years, there have been heights of jubilation and valleys of disappointment, yet Clint continued to fight the good fight.

This character's stories are currently being published by M25:20 Media. The year 2014-2015 looks to be the break out year for Matthew Cross. I've always thought that Faith Walker was a very strong Christian character and will have a major impact in the marketplace as the Lord opens up doors of opportunity. And with the support of his wife Shawntrice (who happens to be the president of M25:20 Media, Inc.), there are no limits to the levels of success that *Faith Walker* can achieve. But that is because Clint D. Johnson is a faith walker.

For 24 years he has stayed focused on the purpose that God has given him in spite of difficulties, obstacles, and discouragement. That perseverance is what embodies this walk of faith, so in essence we are all faith walkers, trusting in His promises that He is faithful about fulfilling our lives.

Ralph E. Miley
President
Christian Comic Arts Society

EXPRESSIONS FROM THE CREATOR

When I was 26 years old sitting in church I watched the pastor while he preached a fiery message. As he commanded the pulpit, his tailored ecclesiastical robe swirled about him. It was eye-catching and stunning and complemented the powerful presentation. I saw a superhero reaching out to save souls and enlighten people about the goodness of God. Needless to say I was blown away that day. Christ reached me in a deeper manner while stirring up my imagination. That image was the inspiration for what is now the Faith Walker's Garment of Praise.

This collection of the priestly patrolman's adventures were featured online and in print at different locations and times. Sensitive topics like human trafficking, drug use, vigilantism, and, yes, the wages of sin are explored in these vibrant pages. With bonus and extended content added, M25:20 Media takes the mantle to move Matthew Cross to the next realm. In the merger of holiness and heroics my hope and prayer is that you enjoy and share these adventures of faith, triumph, and warfare.

God bless you,
Elder Clint D. Johnson

TABLE OF CONTENTS

Sin Assassins

"THE FAITH WALKER IS STILL ONLY MORTAL! STILL A MAN. WITHOUT THE PROTECTION OF HIS GOD HE IS MOST VULNERABLE! HE IS LOST!

HE IS A SINNER SAVED BY GRACE. STILL A SINNER. ONE DAY HE SHALL SLIP.

ONE DAY HE WILL FALL FROM GRACE. THAT DAY WE WILL BE THERE.

WE WILL BE THERE TO CAPTURE HIS SOUL SO DECLARES

SINN AND THE SIN ASSASSINS!

HA HA HA HA HA HA HA HA!

The LORD IS MY LIGHT AND MY SALVATION; WHOM SHALL I FEAR? THE LORD IS THE STRENGTH OF MY LIFE; OF WHOM SHALL I BE AFRAID?*

WHEN THE WICKED, EVEN MINE ENEMIES AND MY FOES, CAME UPON ME TO EAT UP MY FLESH, THEY STUMBLED AND FELL.

THOUGH A HOST SHOULD ENCAMP AGAINST ME, MY HEART SHALL NOT FEAR: THOUGH WAR SHOULD RISE AGAINST ME, IN THIS WILL I BE CONFIDENT.

*PSALM 27:1-3

SURELY NOT THE END

Deliver Us from Evil

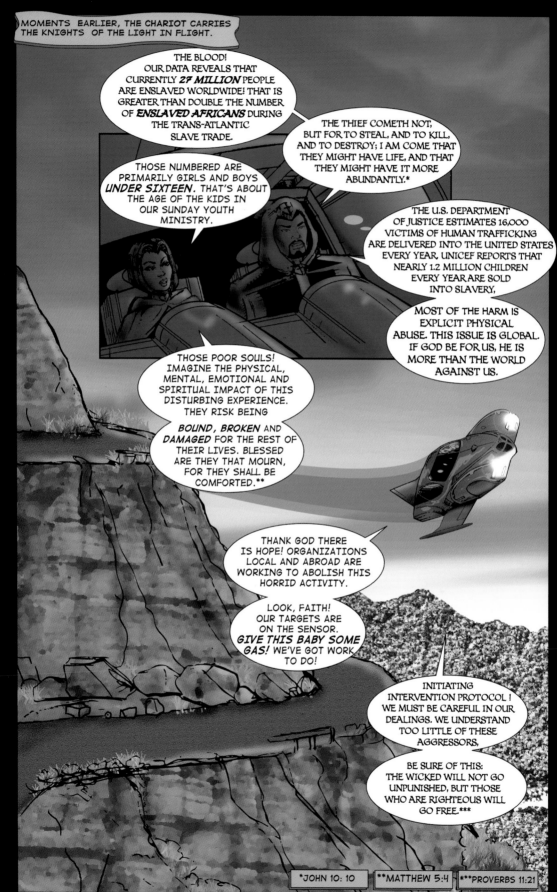

LORD, I'M TERRIFIED. I CAN'T BELIEVE THAT THIS IS ACTUALLY HAPPENING TO US. I REMEMBER YOUR WORD SAYS THAT YOU WOULD NEVER LEAVE US OR FORSAKE US.

LORD PLEASE ANSWER MY PRAYERS...

JUST ABOVE THE HIDEOUT...

TRACKING SENSORS HAVE CONFIRMED TARGET LOCATION. HEAT SIGNATURES MATCH THOSE OF ALLEGED TARGETS. INITIATE NEXT PHASE OF PROTOCOL.

KNIGHT GLIDE IN MOTION. ENABLING CLOAK OF COMPASSION GHOST-MODE FOR STEALTH OPTIMIZATION.

KNIGHT GLIDE IN MOTION. ENABLING GARMENT OF PRAISE GHOST-MODE FOR STEALTH OPTIMIZATION.

SLEEP BALM DEPLOYED.

TARGET SUBDUED.

BE ADVISED, LIGHT KNIGHTS ENTERING TARGET LOCATION.

PREPARED FOR BEST POSSIBLE SCENARIO. SAFETY OF CAPTIVES IS OF OPTIMAL IMPORTANCE. NO COMPROMISE.

FAITH WALKER TO W.O.R.D. TECH BASE. LANDING AFFIRMED.

ONE ASSAILANT ON OUTER PREMISE.

POPF!

INITIAL DIRECTIVE: SET CAPTIVES FREE. IT'S ON.

ASSESSMENT OF THE SITUATION REQUIRES BACK UP MEASURES. REINFORCEMENT EN ROUTE.

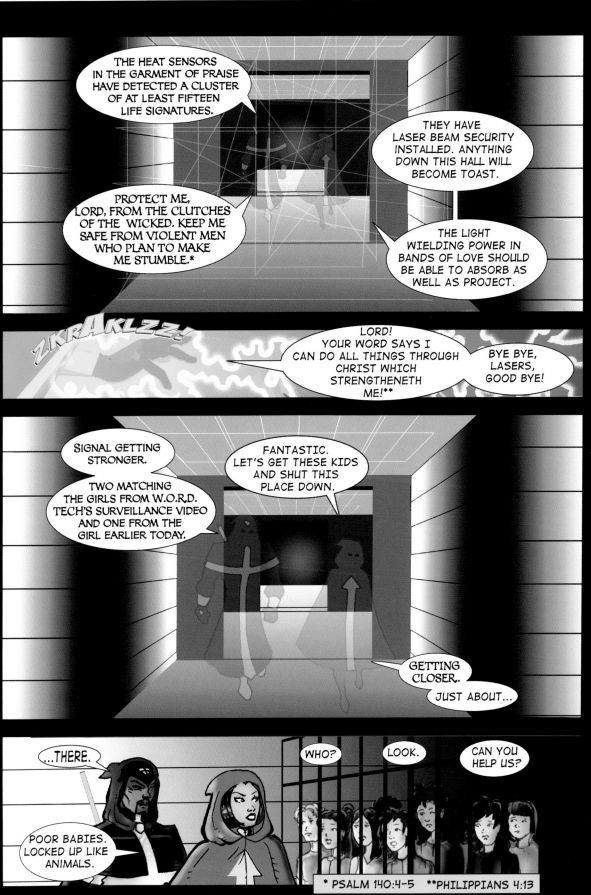

BZZZHANG!

THIS IS YOURS... HOPE TO BURST YOUR BALL AND BREAK YOUR CHAIN! TIME TO SHUT IT DOWN!

YOUR INJUSTICE IS A CRIME AGAINST HUMANITY AND HEAVEN!

THE EARTH IS THE LORD'S AND THE FULLNESS THEREOF AND ALL THOSE WHO DWELL THERE WITHIN!*

YOUR ACTIONS HAVE STAINED THE GLOBE! NEVERTHELESS, THERE IS HOPE.

KZZZHANK!

*1 CORINTHIANS 10:26

AGGH! YOU CANNOT HOLD US FOREVER.

NO, BUT HE WHO HOLDS FOREVER CAN HOLD YOU FOR ETERNITY.

OOOHH!

THE CAPTORS HAVE BECOME THE CAPTIVES.

YES. THESE TWO ARE DONE. THE AUTHORITIES ARE JUST OUTSIDE.

Sins of the Father

HR1R

THE CITY OF LOS COSMOS WHERE WE FIND CONCRETE GARDEN MIDDLE SCHOOL, AN INNER CITY EDUCATIONAL INSTITUTION WHERE THE STUDENTS THRIVE ON HIGH ACHIEVEMENT REGARDLESS OF THE NEIGHBORING UNDERSERVED COMMUNITY CONDITIONS.

IT IS THE START OF THE LUNCH PERIOD AS A GROUP OF HUNGRY EIGHTH GRADERS CONGREGATE IN THE STONY CAMPUS COURTYARD.

BENNY B, YOU'RE AMAZING! IT'S A WONDER YOU KEEP COMING TO CLASS EVERYDAY WITH SO MUCH GOING ON IN YOUR LIFE.

YEAH, SWEETIE, IT'S BEEN TOUGH. WITH SO MUCH HAPPENING TO MY POPS, IT'S HARD TO THINK STRAIGHT SOMETIMES.
I HAVE TO BELIEVE THAT EVERYTHING IS GOING TO BE ALRIGHT.

DONT TRIP, MY BROTHER.
ME AND THE FAM HAVE BEEN CALLING OUT YOU AND YOUR DAD ON THE PRAYER LINE. THE WORD SAYS TO PRAY WITHOUT CEASING—
I HAVE YOU ON SPEED DIAL!
Y' FEEL ME?

I FEEL YOU, BABY SAINT.
I REALLY APPRECIATE YOU HOLLER'N AT GOD FOR ME LIKE THAT.

RRRRRRRRRRR!

ON THE REAL, I DON'T KNOW HOW I KEEP GOING. I SHOULD HAVE LOST IT BY NOW. MUST BE YOUR PRAYERS.

I'M REALLY SCARED FOR MY POPS.

KEEP YOUR HEAD UP, BE STRONG AND COURAGEOUS

RRRRRRRRRRR!

WHAAAAA?

HUH?

RRRRRRRRRRRR!

GOOD AFTERNOON, YOUNG MR. BROOKS. YOU BARE AN UNCANNY RESEMBLANCE TO YOUR FATHER.

YOU REMIND ME SO MUCH OF A CRIMINAL.

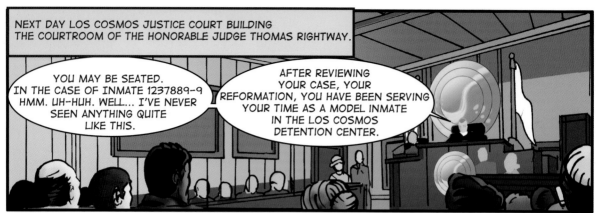

NEXT DAY LOS COSMOS JUSTICE COURT BUILDING
THE COURTROOM OF THE HONORABLE JUDGE THOMAS RIGHTWAY.

YOU MAY BE SEATED. IN THE CASE OF INMATE 1237889-9 HMM. UH-HUH. WELL... I'VE NEVER SEEN ANYTHING QUITE LIKE THIS.

AFTER REVIEWING YOUR CASE, YOUR REFORMATION, YOU HAVE BEEN SERVING YOUR TIME AS A MODEL INMATE IN THE LOS COSMOS DETENTION CENTER.

APPARENTLY YOU HAVE FAMILY THAT SUPPORTS YOU AND GAINFUL EMPLOYMENT LINED UP.

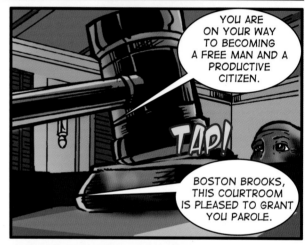

YOU ARE ON YOUR WAY TO BECOMING A FREE MAN AND A PRODUCTIVE CITIZEN.

TAP!

BOSTON BROOKS, THIS COURTROOM IS PLEASED TO GRANT YOU PAROLE.

I OBJECT! THIS HEARING IS A CIRCUS!

YAHOO! HOORAY! YES! THANK YOU ,JESUS!

THE SYSTEM IS SO CORRUPT THAT YOU WOULD ALLOW THIS CANCER TO SPREAD HIS VIRUS FURTHER MORE?

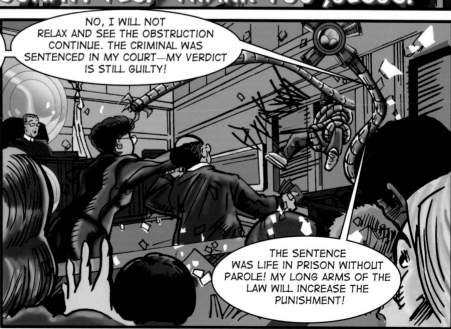

NO, I WILL NOT RELAX AND SEE THE OBSTRUCTION CONTINUE. THE CRIMINAL WAS SENTENCED IN MY COURT—MY VERDICT IS STILL GUILTY!

THE SENTENCE WAS LIFE IN PRISON WITHOUT PAROLE! MY LONG ARMS OF THE LAW WILL INCREASE THE PUNISHMENT!

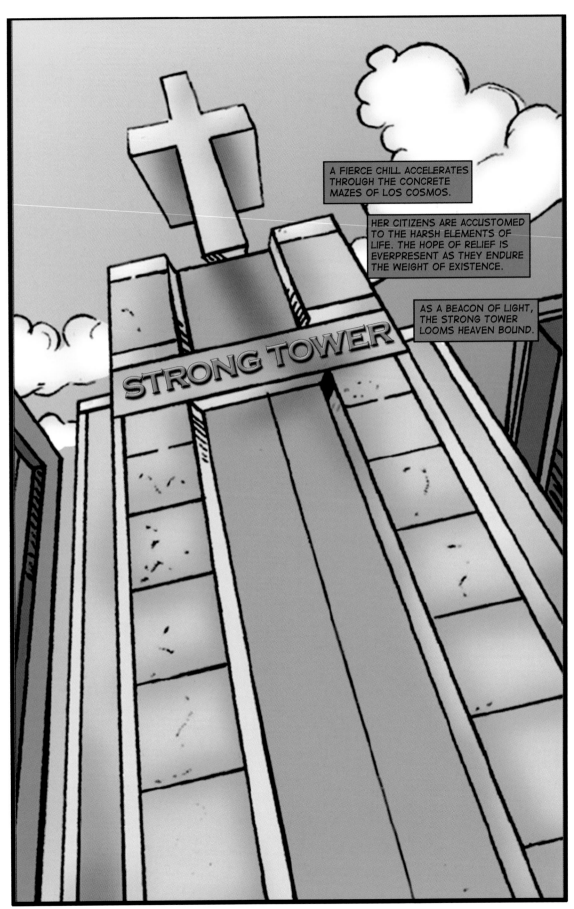

A FIERCE CHILL ACCELERATES THROUGH THE CONCRETE MAZES OF LOS COSMOS.

HER CITIZENS ARE ACCUSTOMED TO THE HARSH ELEMENTS OF LIFE. THE HOPE OF RELIEF IS EVERPRESENT AS THEY ENDURE THE WEIGHT OF EXISTENCE.

AS A BEACON OF LIGHT, THE STRONG TOWER LOOMS HEAVEN BOUND.

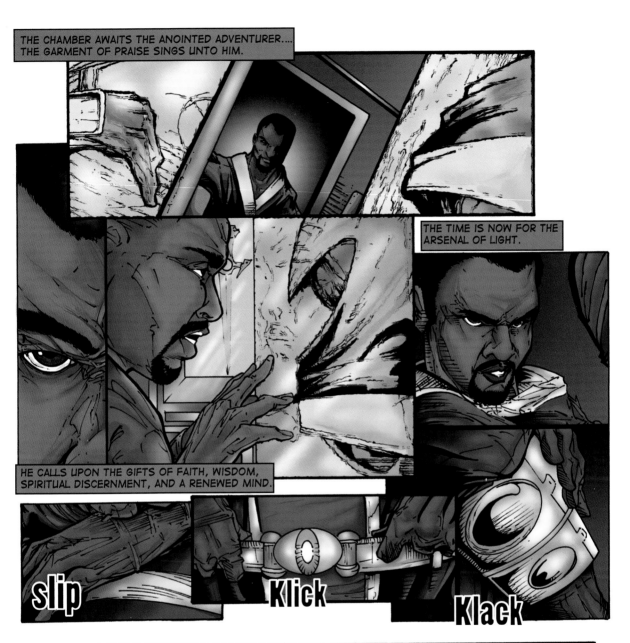

THE LIGHT KNIGHT KNOWN AS
FAITH WALKER!

THE CRIME SCENE: THE WIDE ROAD DISTRICT CORRECTIONS FACILITY. THE SENIOR OFFICER IS *LIEUTENANT ROCKA* OF THE LOS COSMOS POLICE DEPARTMENT.

THE LOS COSMOS POLICE DEPARTMENT IS WELL PREPARED. ROCKA? I DIDN'T KNOW SHE WOULD BE HERE.

ALL OFFICERS ARE IN POSITION SIR, EH, LT.

GOOD. CARRY ON, HMMM?

OKAY?

LT., WE HAVE SPOTTED A PECULIAR SPECTATOR ON THE ROOF ACROSS THE STREET. WHAT DO YOU SUGGEST?

NOTHING. HE WILL COME TO US.

HIS AGILE FORM GRACEFULLY DESCENDS INTO THE TURBULENT TERRITORY HE WAS BORN TO PROTECT.

OH GREAT! THE SUNDAY SCHOOL TEACHER HAS ARRIVED!

STAND DOWN; I AM UNDER THE AUTHORITY OF THE W.O.R.D. TECH LIGHT KNIGHTS.

WHAT ARE YOU GOING TO DO? TEACH HIM THE TEN COMMANDMENTS?

IF GIVEN MY WAY? YES. I'M PREPARED TO GET INVOLVED TO GET THIS SITUATION UNDER CONTROL.

LIKE YOU DID WITH MY *SISTER?* THE ONLY REASON YOU ARE HERE IS BECAUSE THIS GUY HAS *DEMANDED YOU.* THE FINE OFFICERS OF LOS COSMOS CAN HANDLE THIS SITUATION, WE DON'T NEED *YOUR KIND* HERE. ESPECIALLY NOT YOU, CROSS.

LOOK ANGELA, YOUR SISTER AND I ...THAT WAS A LONG TIME AGO. I CAN'T BLAME YOU FOR BEING ANGRY. I'M NOT EVEN *THE SAME MAN.* A NEW CREATURE.

THIS IS MY *DESTINY:* TO AID IN THIS WAR AGAINST DARKNESS NO MATTER *HOW* IT MANIFEST ITSELF... NOW ALLOW ME I MUST BE ABOUT MY FATHER'S BUSINESS.

CROSS! CEASE THE STRIFE WITH ROCKA! YOU ARE HERE ON A MISSION.

THE PERPETRATOR IS AN EX JUDGE WHOSE SENTENCING BECAME HARSH AND OFTEN QUESTIONABLE.

THE ACCUSED HAS ARRIVED. COURT IS NOW IN SESSION AS WE ENGAGE THE TRAIL OF THE FAITH WALKER! WE SHALL SEE JUSTICE ADMINISTERED BY THE VERDICT OF JUDGE JONAH.

JONAH WILSON WAS ONE OF THE BEST IN THE LEGAL SYSTEM. HE WAS HIGHLY RESPECTED IN LEGAL CIRCLES. FAIR AND EXACT.

IT IS JOY TO THE JUST TO DO JUDGMENT: BUT DESTRUCTION SHALL BE TO THE WORKERS OF INIQUITY.

PROVERBS 21:15

HE IS OPERATING INDEPENDENTLY OF THE SYSTEM THAT HE ONCE SERVED. THE JUDGE HAS TAKEN THE DEATH ROW INMATE BASHER BROOKS AND HIS SON AS PRISONERS ADDING TO HIS WILD VENDETTA.

DOTH OUR LAW JUDGE ANY MAN, BEFORE IT HEARS HIM, AND KNOWS WHAT HE DOETH?

JOHN 7:51

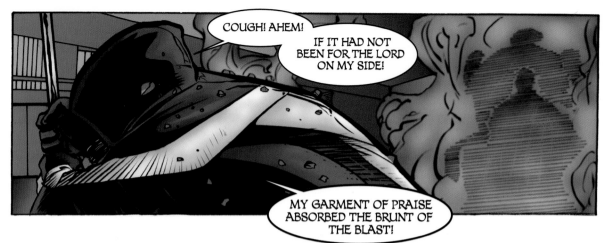

I HAVE STUDIED YOU, ANTICIPATED YOU.

YOU APPEAR TO BE SO FAITHFUL TO THE CAUSE. WHERE WAS YOUR ZEAL AND VIGILANCE IN THE CASE OF ONE YOUTH? ONE SOUL LYING MOTIONLESS AND FORSAKEN IN A HOSPITAL BED.

A SOUL NAMED RICHARD WILSON.

RICHIE "RAZORBLADE" WILSON?

IT'S ABOUT *JUSTICE*, MATTHEW. BEFORE HIS PRIME, HE LIES IN A COMA!

YOU FAILED TO SHARE *THE GOSPEL* WITH HIM.

NOW HE IS *TRAPPED* BETWIXT AND BETWEEN THE GATES OF LIFE AND DEATH.

WHAT IS THIS ABOUT?

WELL, MATTHEW, SOURCES SAY THE TWO OF YOU KINDLED A STRONG BOND. MY REPORTS INDICATE THAT YOU "RAN THE STREETS" TOGETHER. ENVIOUS MEN WERE AT YOUR THROATS WHILE FEMALES WERE AT YOUR BECK AND CALL.

ON THAT DREADFUL NIGHT RICHARD BORROWED YOUR JACKET TO PROTECT HIM FROM THE COLD OF NIGHT.

IT SHOULD HAVE BEEN *YOU*, MATTHEW. IF HE AWAKES ON THIS SIDE OF HEAVEN...

NOT REALIZING THAT YOUR GARMENT WOULD DRAW THE FORCES OF NIGHT TO HIM.

...THE LAKE OF FIRE IS WHERE HE WILL SPEND ETERNITY! *GUILTY!*

SNAP! IT'S MAD MAC MATT!

THE VERMIN MISTOOK RICHARD FOR YOU, MATTHEW.

GAME OVER!

BLAM! BLAM! BLAM! BLAM!

BELIEVING THAT WE'RE ERADICATING THE CITY OF THE BOASTFUL "MAD MAC MATT"...

... THEY PROCEEDED TO EXECUTE THE WRONG MAN. MY *SON* NEVER STOOD A CHANCE AS THE DEMONS AWAIT HIS MISGUIDED SOUL!

MY *SON*.

YES. I WAS DOUBLE MINDED. UNSTABLE IN ALL MY WAYS. I MISSED THE MARK.

I AM SO SORRY.

SORRY? WHO KNOWS? GUILTY AS SIN? DEFINITELY. ALL BECAUSE A MAN WHO KNEW GOD. DID NOT SHARE GOD ANOTHER MAY NEVER KNOW HIM.

YOU ARE OF THE CHOSEN. *DESTROYING* YOU WILL NOT SERVE MY PURPOSE.

FOR *HIS* OWN TO BE ABSENT FROM THE BODY IS TO BE PRESENT WITH THE LORD. I REFUSE TO MAKE YOU A MARTYR.

"...YET HE WILL BY NO MEANS LEAVE THE GUILTY UNPUNISHED,

...VISITING THE INIQUITY OF FATHERS ON THE CHILDREN."

CRIMINALS LIKE *BASHER* AND HIS SEED WILL DO JUST FINE!

OW! HELP! HE IS SQUEEZING ME!

HOLD UP MAN! YOU CAN'T BE SERIOUS!

MY BOY IS INNOCENT. IT AIN'T FAIR!

CRUNCH!

FAIR? IT'S NOT FAIR THAT DAMNATION AWAITS MY SON. IT'S THE LAW, AND I AM THE JUDGE!

IT IS WRITTEN: IF WE CONFESS OUR SINS, HE IS FAITHFUL AND JUST TO FORGIVE US OUR SINS, AND TO CLEANSE US FROM ALL UN-RIGHTEOUSNESS.*

*1 John 1:9 KJV

60

For there is one god, and one mediator also between god and men, the man christ jesus, 1 TIMOTHY 2:5

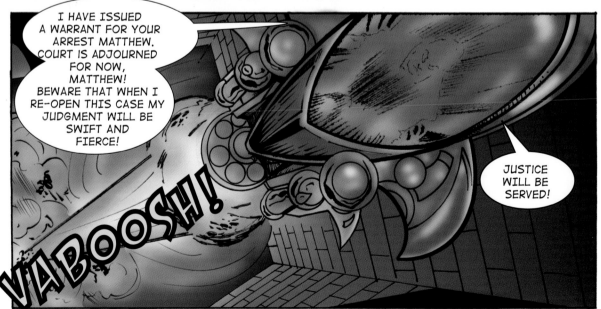

THE END

Smoke and Mirrors

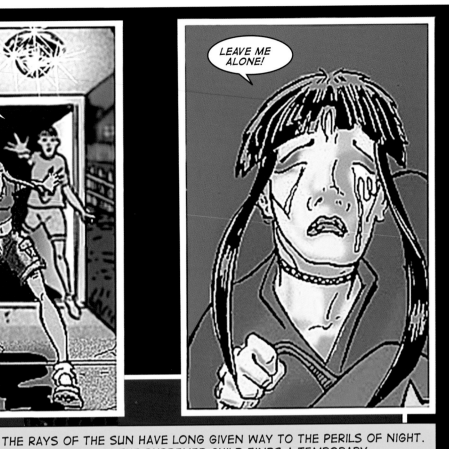

THE RAYS OF THE SUN HAVE LONG GIVEN WAY TO THE PERILS OF NIGHT. MILES FROM HOME THE BURDENED CHILD FINDS A TEMPORARY SOLACE IN A PLACE KNOWN AS THE TEMPLE. A PLACE FOR THE LOST WHO DESPERATELY SEEK TO WORSHIP A FLEETING SENSATION.

HER HEART BEATS RAPIDLY AS SHE APPROACHES THE GATEWAY TO HER DANGEROUS DESTINATION.

PLEASE, I HAVE AN OFFERING FOR THE PREISTESS.

A TERRAIN DIVISIBLE BY **WORKERS OF INIQUITY**, **FORMER WELDERS OF THE THE LIGHT** AND THE COUNTLESS **SOULS** THAT DWELL THERE.

MANY HAVE SUBMITTED THIER SOULS AND HAVE BEEN CONSUMED BY THE FORCES THAT THRIVE BEYOND THIS GATEWAY.

SLAM!

*II CORINTHIANS 7:1

THE END.

Keeper of the City

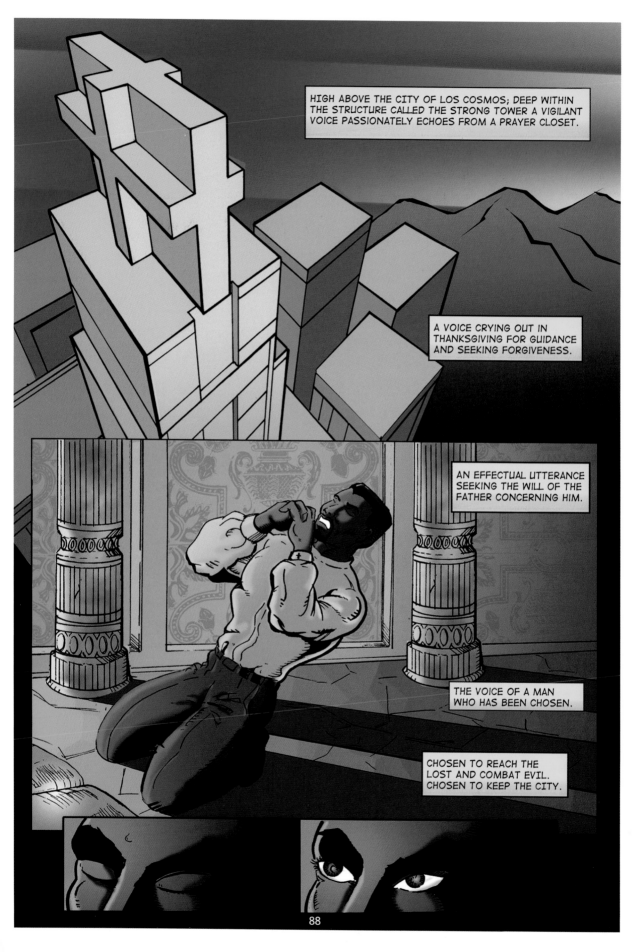

HIGH ABOVE THE CITY OF LOS COSMOS; DEEP WITHIN THE STRUCTURE CALLED THE STRONG TOWER A VIGILANT VOICE PASSIONATELY ECHOES FROM A PRAYER CLOSET.

A VOICE CRYING OUT IN THANKSGIVING FOR GUIDANCE AND SEEKING FORGIVENESS.

AN EFFECTUAL UTTERANCE SEEKING THE WILL OF THE FATHER CONCERNING HIM.

THE VOICE OF A MAN WHO HAS BEEN CHOSEN.

CHOSEN TO REACH THE LOST AND COMBAT EVIL. CHOSEN TO KEEP THE CITY.

TO BE CONTINUED IN *THE ART OF WARFARE*

DATA FILES

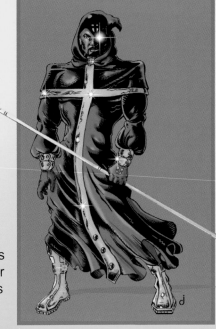

The Faith Walker
Age: 29
Height: 6 ft.1 in.
Weight: 220 lbs.
Eyes: Brown
Hair: Black
Real name: Matthew Adam Cross
Former occupation: Minister
Identity: Publicly known
Legal status: Citizenship of the United States
Place of birth: OurFair Community
Marital Status: Single
Group Affiliation: First Watch, a division of Western Operations Research and Defense Technologies. (A specialized Elite Sector of the FBI) Rank: Field Agent, GS 13 (Federal Status) Emphasis to confront and contain supernatural/occult/paranormal threats.

Home: The Strong Tower, City of Los Cosmos
Base of operations: W.O.R.D. Tech Dome of Destiny, Los Cosmos

Traits: As the son of Southern ministers, Matthew Cross had a strict upbringing. He is a quick witted gentleman, genuinely a big picture optimistic, courageous, and faithful. He is caring and wise beyond his years. Matthew likes writing poetry.

Strength Level: Faith Walker has Olympic athlete level agility, strength, speed, endurance, and reaction time. He is a trained Federal Agent accomplished in armed and unarmed combat. He's trained in boxing and mixed martial arts, in particular Aikido. He is known to incorporate parkour into his agile movements. A noted physical attribute is his majestic gracefulness. While not superhuman, he is as strong as a human being can be. He can lift (press) a maximum of 700 pounds with supreme effort.

Known Supernatural Powers: Faith Walker is a spirit driven student and teacher of the Word, possessing an astonishing recall of the Holy Scriptures. His noted traits are love, unyielding faith, and wisdom. His gifts also include Spiritual Discernment (The Eye of Fire) that alerts him to the presences of angelic and demonic forces. Discernment allows him to glimpse into hearts of men. His anointing grants a higher resistance to demonic influence and the mysterious faith factor in times of grave peril. Cross's measure of faith taps into the supernatural to produce miraculous super human results.

Weapons: W.O.R.D. Technologies supplies him with a series of combat fitted items. He wears the purple and gold spidersilk uniform which is referred to as the Garment of Praise. Faith Walker is equipped with The Arsenal of Light that includes: (ROA) Rod of Aaron, The Crossbow, Fisherman's net, Ghost-Mode invisibility capabilities, and an array of bible themed gadgets and gizmos. He drives/flies a combat ready vehicle called the Chariot.

Limitations: Faith Walker is subject to all human vulnerabilities.

Pencil Cover Concepts by Steven Butler

Pencil Art by Clint D. Johnson

Cover Pencil Art by Clint D. Johnson

MATTHEW CROSS'S FAVORITE FAITH SCRIPTURES

- Now faith is the substance of things hoped for, the evidence of things not seen. (Hebrews 11:1)

- (For we walk by faith, not by sight:) (2 Corinthians 5:7)

- So then faith cometh by hearing, and hearing by the word of God.   (Romans 10:17)

- But ye, beloved, building up yourselves on your most holy faith, praying in the Holy Ghost, (Jude 1:20)

- For we through the Spirit wait for the hope of righteousness by faith. (Galations 5:5)

- Fight the good fight of faith, lay hold on eternal life, whereunto thou art also called, and hast professed a good profession before many witnesses. (I Timothy 6:12)

- Examine yourselves, whether ye be in the faith; prove your own selves. Know ye not your own selves, how that Jesus Christ is in you, except ye be reprobates? (2 Corithians 13:5)

- And he that doubteth is damned if he eat, because he eateth not of faith: for whatsoever is not of faith is sin. (Romans 14:23)

- Moreover it is required in stewards, that a man be found faithful. (I Corithians 4:2)

- And beside this, giving all diligence, add to your faith virtue; and to virtue knowledge; And to knowledge temperance; and to temperance patience; and to patience godliness; And to godliness brotherly kindness; and to brotherly kindness charity. (2 Peter 1:5-7)

- Looking unto Jesus the author and finisher of our faith; who for the joy that was set before him endured the cross, despising the shame, and is set down at the right hand of the throne of God. (Hebrews 12:2)

- And righteousness shall be the girdle of his loins, and faithfulness the girdle of his reins. (Isaiah 11:5)

- O love the LORD, all ye his saints: for the LORD preserveth the faithful, and plentifully rewardeth the proud doer. (Psalm 31:23)

- I have fought a good fight, I have finished my course, I have kept the faith: (2 Timothy 4:7)

- Fear none of those things which thou shalt suffer: behold, the devil shall cast some of you into prison, that ye may be tried; and ye shall have tribulation ten days: be thou faithful unto death, and I will give thee a crown of life. (Revelation 2:10)

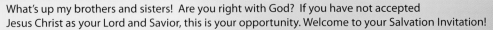
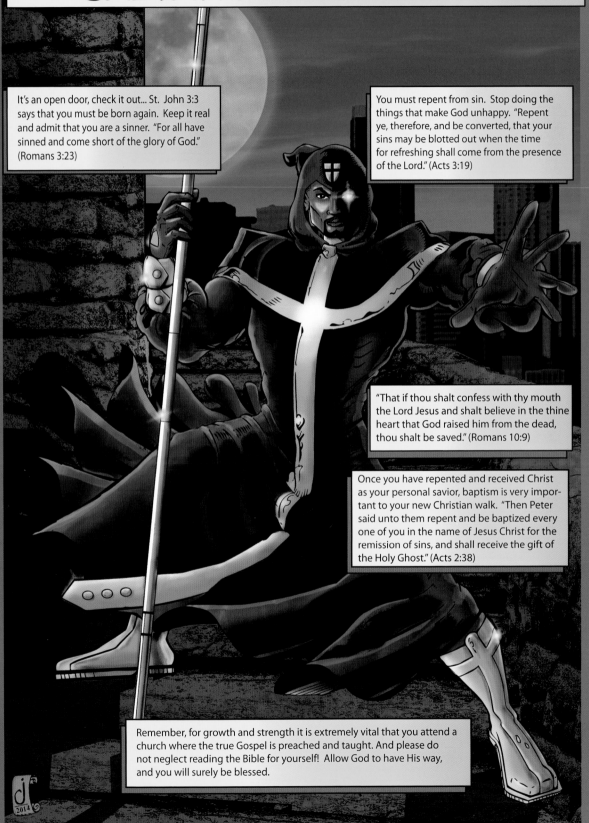

FAITH WALKER PLEDGE PAGE

In May of 2015 many of you pledged to our Kickstarter campaign to print more copies of The Faith Walker Collected. Because of your generous and enthusiastic pledges, this book now exists. Thank you for walking on this journey with us. This page is dedicated to our supporters. Many blessings to you. Clint & The Crew.

2121 ToonNetwork
Kibibi Ajanku
Byron & Melvenna Allen
Karl Alstaetter
Dawud Anyabwile
John Araujo
Jermell Slice Atkins
Betty Badgett
Moses Ball
Matthew Blackwell
Larry Poncho Brown
Jeremy Scott Browning
Bruce
Brett Burner
Dana & Sharon Burrell
CO
David Campbell
Sergio Cariello
Medardo Carranza
Norris Connic
Garnell Cooper
Leonard & La Tanya Cross
Cyiworldwide.com
Shaterra Davidson
Theresa Dawson
Demetris
Gabriel Dill
Rosalynd Divinity
Mr. Charles & Sonji Dorsey Jr.
Empowered Church
   International
The Eskridge Family
Faithseed.org
Remi Fayomi a.k.a.
   Negromaestro
Carmi Fellwock
Toni Flennoy
Gale Frazier
Tim Gagnon
Papa & Nana Garcia

Geoff
James & Christine Gipson
Bernard Gravel
Gwendoyln Grissom
Wayne Guillary
Jose A. Guillen
Rachel Harris
Derwin Henderson
Mr. Heroic
Alan Herbert of HBComics
Mary J.
Nigel & Ivanna J.
Jena
JoEllen
DeNay Johnson
Lee DJ Flash Johnson
Linda Johnson
Joann Jolley
Jason Jones
JunkRobot
Lance Oliver Keeble
Pete King
Sandra Kinji
Tony Kittrell / Advent Comics
Shandra Koger
Dan Lawlis
Steven M. Lyles,
   ClearVision Communications
Dr. Mark Marshall
Phillip & Tammy Marshall
Justin Martin,
   R-Squared Comicz
Bryan Mero
Michael
Randy Michaelsen
Pastor Ralph Miley
Katherine Mitchell
Quinn Moore
Marc Moran
Bryce Morgan

Loretta Myers
Kenneth Nelson
Steve & Mary Lou Newborn
John W. Otte
Perry
Tyrone Petrie
Demetris Pierson
Danny Potts
The Randle Crew
Caesar & Monica Rodriguez
Scott Mitchell Rosenberg/
   Platinum Studios
Andrew Rowland
Ingrid Salinas
Paul Scott
Luis Serrano
Bonita Shanklin
Shawntrice
Matt Simanski
Skijelli
Lance Smith
Noah & Eli Spencer
Daniel Stewart
Quenton Tatum
Derrick Tinsley
Bishop George A. Todd Jr.
Melchizedek Todd
Ashley Turner
Vangie
Ms. Vivica
Perry Watkins Sr.
Shannon Wendler
Jim & Suzy West
Clarence Williams
Dan Williams
John Wimmer
Kevin Yong
Pastor Deborah R. Young